AUDITION SONGS
COUNTRY

CW00395175

WISE PUBLICATIONS
PART OF THE MUSIC SALES GROUP
LONDON / NEW YORK / PARIS / SYDNEY / COPENHAGEN / BERLIN / MADRID / HONG KONG / TOKYO

Published by
WISE PUBLICATIONS
14-15 Berners Street, London W1T 3LJ, UK.

Exclusive Distributors:
MUSIC SALES LIMITED
Distribution Centre, Newmarket Road,
Bury St Edmunds, Suffolk IP33 3YB, UK.
MUSIC SALES PTY LIMITED
20 Resolution Drive,
Caringbah, NSW 2229, Australia.

Order No. AM996897
ISBN 978-1-84938-539-8
This book © Copyright 2010 Wise Publications,
a division of Music Sales Limited.

Music edited by Jenni Wheeler
Printed in the EU

CD recorded, mixed and mastered by Jonas Persson
Backing tracks arranged by Paul Honey
Guitars by Arthur Dick

BLANKET ON THE GROUND

WORDS & MUSIC BY ROGER BOWLING

ground.

2.Oh, re - mem - ber how___ ex -

-ci - ted   we used to get___ when love was young?___

That old moon___ was our___ best bud - dy,

9

we could-n't wait___ for night to come.___

Now you know___ you still ex - cite me.

I know you love___ me like I am.___

Just once more I wish you'd love___ me on the

THE END OF THE WORLD

WORDS BY SYLVIA DEE
MUSIC BY ARTHUR KENT

1. Why____ does the sun____ go on shin - ing?____

Why____ does the sea rush to shore?

Don't   they___   know___   it's the   end___   of the world,   'cause

you   don't   love   me___   an - y - more?

2. Why___   do the birds___   go on   sing - ing?___

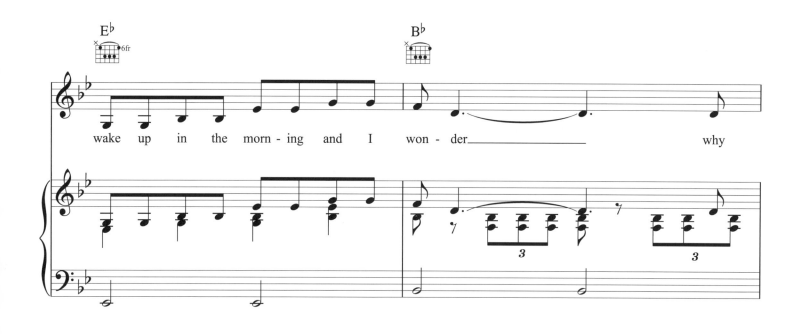

wake up in the morn - ing and I won - der_____ why

ev-'ry-thing's_ the same___ as it was. I can't un-der-stand,___ no I

can't un-der-stand how life goes on the way it does.

Why____ does my heart____ go on beat - ing?____
(Vocal spoken on repeat)

Why____ do these eyes____ of mine cry?

Don't they____ know____ it's the end____ of the world?____ It
(Sung)

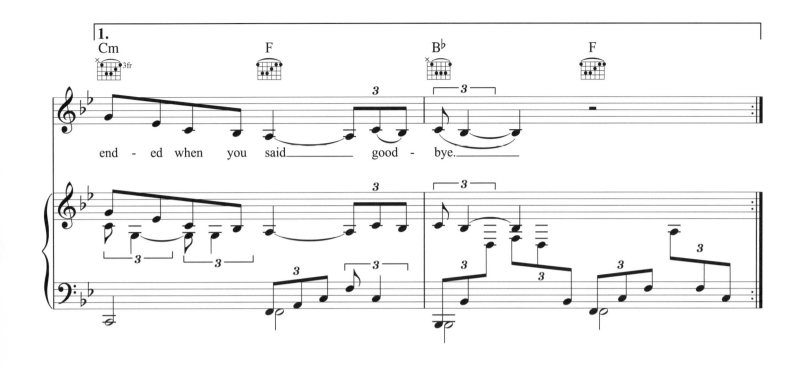

end - ed when you said_____ good - bye._____

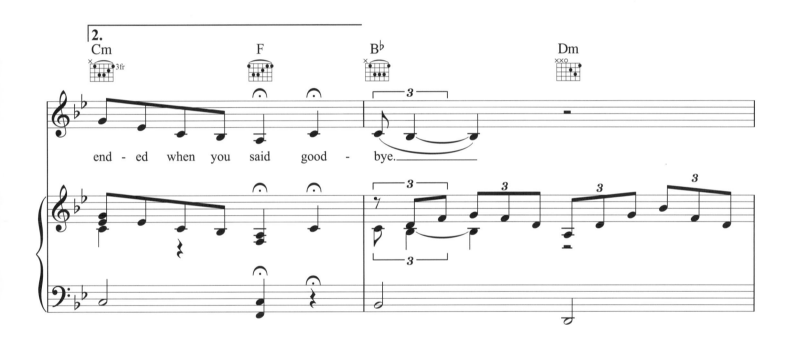

end - ed when you said good - bye._____

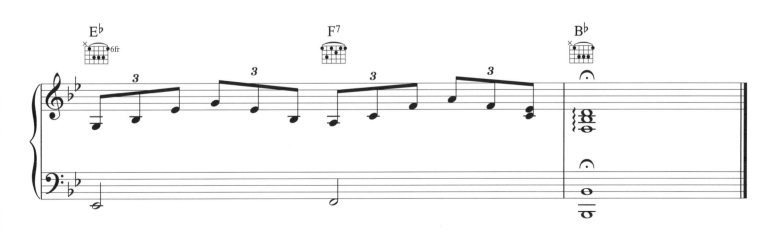

HOW DO I LIVE

WORDS & MUSIC BY DIANE WARREN

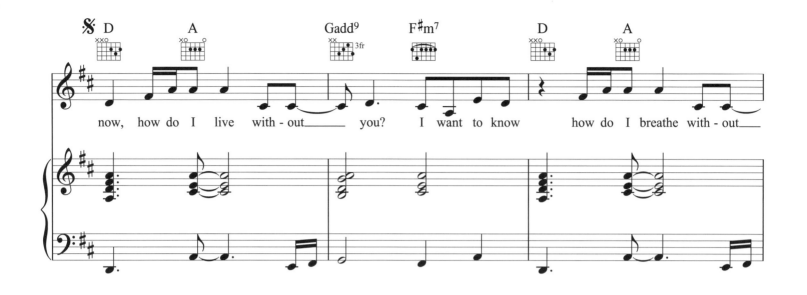

now, how do I live with-out_____ you? I want to know how do I breathe with-out_____

_____ you? If you ev-er_____ go_____ how do I ev-er, ev-er sur-vive?

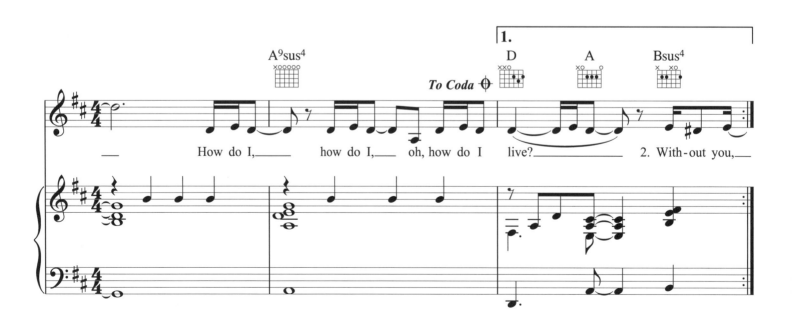

How do I,_____ how do I,____ oh, how do I live?_____ 2. With-out you,____

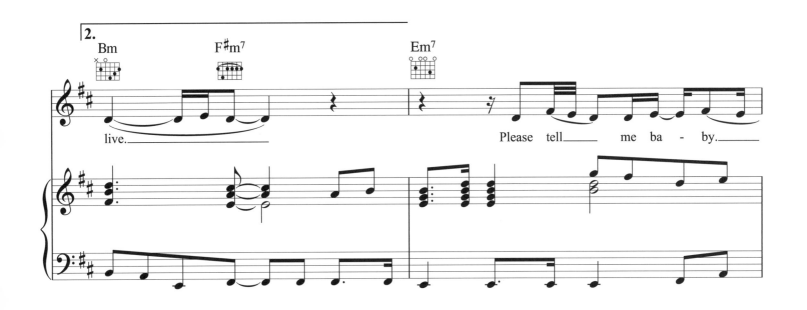

live._____ Please tell_____ me ba - by._____

How do I go on_____ if

you ev - er leave?_____ Oh, ba - by you would take a - way ev - 'ry - thing.__

JOLENE

WORDS & MUSIC BY DOLLY PARTON

please don't take him e - ven though you___ can.___

Jo - lene.

Jo - lene.___

Repeat ad lib. to fade

29

I'LL NEVER FALL IN LOVE AGAIN

WORDS BY HAL DAVID
MUSIC BY BURT BACHARACH

never fall in love a - gain,

I'll   nev - er   fall   in   love a -

1.

- gain.

2, 3.

- gain.   Don't   tell me what it's

ROSE GARDEN

WORDS & MUSIC BY JOE SOUTH

SWEET DREAMS

WORDS & MUSIC BY DON GIBSON

I should know I'll nev-er wear your ring.

I should hate you the whole_ night_

through, in-stead of hav-ing sweet dreams a-bout

can't I for-get the past, start lov-ing some-one new. In-

-stead of hav-ing sweet dreams a-bout you.

TALKING IN YOUR SLEEP

WORDS & MUSIC BY ROGER COOK & BOBBY WOOD

47

YOU'RE STILL THE ONE

WORDS & MUSIC BY SHANIA TWAIN & R.J. LANGE

WHEN YOU SAY NOTHING AT ALL
WORDS & MUSIC BY DON SCHLITZ & PAUL OVERSTREET

52

123456789